Underwater Scilly

by Tim Allsop and Anna Cawthray

Marshfield Underwater Publications, Scilly

First published April 2009
By Marshfield Underwater Publications
Nornour, Higher Town, St Martin's, Isles of Scilly TR25 0QL

Underwater photographs by Tim Allsop
Text by Anna Cawthray
Maps by Jenny Buckland

Copyright © Tim Allsop and Anna Cawthray 2009

All photographs © Tim Allsop except pages 75 and 94 © John Ives
ISBN 978 0 9561874 0 6

Designed by Visualdirection, printed by Purbrooks
Gresham Way
Wimbledon Park
London, SW19 8ED

www.visualdirection.co.uk
www.purbrooks.co.uk

Printed alcohol free using vegetable based inks. Paper is made from wood pulp from
sustainable sources and the finished product is FSC accredited.

Acknowledgements
The authors would like to thank Jock, Sharon and Emily for their assistance in finding new dive
sites. John for the use of his three photos and Allen and Sarah for help with identification.
Thanks also to Clare, Martin and Jan at Purbrooks for designing and printing the book.

Tim would particularly like to thank Viv, and Anna her family, for always being there.

Contents

Introduction

The Isles of Scilly are an archipelago lying 28 miles to the south west of Land's End, Cornwall, see map overleaf. There are five inhabited islands with a resident population of approximately 2,000 people. There are also hundreds of smaller uninhabited islands and rocks. Due to their location, the islands are famous for their shipwrecks. Add to this, stunning and varied marine life and often exceptionally clear water and it's easy to see why Scilly is one of the best places to dive in Britain.

Ask any visitor who has been to Scilly to describe the islands in just one word and the same adjectives - stunning, beautiful, unique, amazing, tranquil - would come up time and time again. Ask these same visitors to describe the islands beneath the waves and you'd probably get some very different descriptions - uninteresting, murky, dark, cold. But ask that same question of someone who's dived any of the islands' spectacular dive sites and you would receive a totally different, but much more accurate response. Once again adjectives such as breathtaking, beautiful, colourful and awesome would be their response.

By their very nature, the Isles of Scilly are defined by the sea. Each inhabited island has a distinctive character and the sea dominates island life. The vast majority of the visitors to Scilly do not have the opportunity to encounter the incredible marine life of the islands. They can only marvel at the colours of the shallow waters between the islands, or be in awe of the power of the sea in a storm. But it is not until you've seen beneath the waves that you can truly appreciate all that Scilly has to offer.

This book, therefore, has been produced to provide those not fortunate enough to be able to dive with a glimpse of the incredible beauty that exists on the wrecks and reefs around Scilly. For divers, it's a reminder of all the good things that Scilly has to offer. Where possible, English names have been used to describe the marine life, except for those species that only have Latin names which will be given in italics. This book is not intended to be a guide to the marine life of the islands, but is more a personal selection of images celebrating the incredible underwater beauty of the islands.

The authors Tim Allsop and Anna Cawthray have between them completed well over 4,000 dives on the islands over a period of twenty five years. Their passion for diving the islands and photographing its beautiful marine life continues unabated.

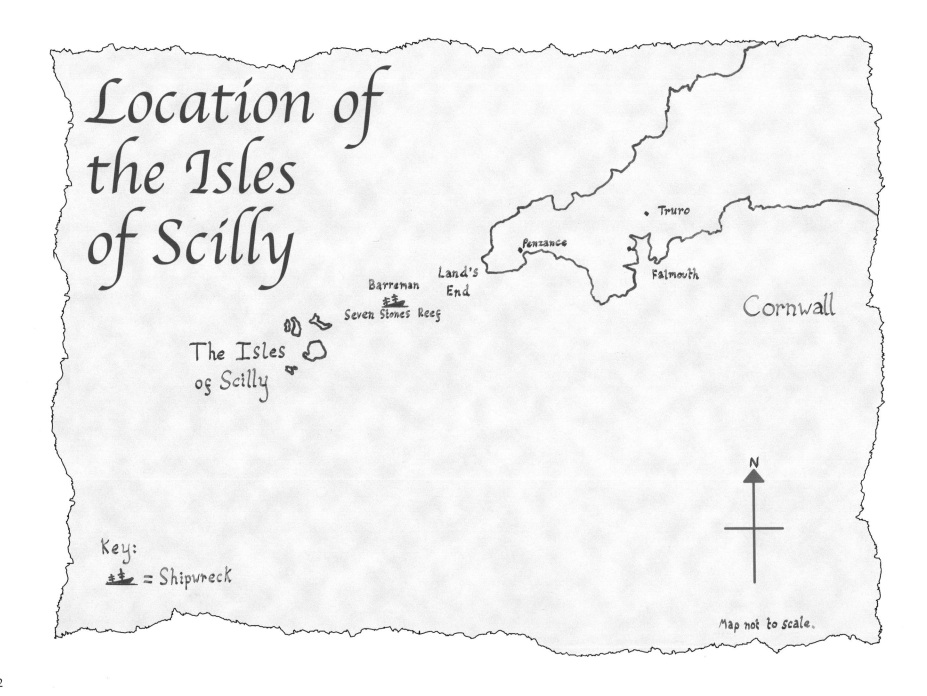

Location of the Isles of Scilly

Cornwall

• Truro

Penzance

Falmouth

Land's End

Barreman

Seven Stones Reef

The Isles of Scilly

Key:
= Shipwreck

N

Map not to scale.

The Isles of Scilly

Menavaur · Round Island · White Island

St. Helen's

Shipman Head · Tean · St. Martin's

Bryher · King Cadwallon

Gweal · Tresco

Eastern Isles

Samson · St. Mary's

Key:
= Shipwreck

Cita

N

Empire

Hollandia · Gugh

Romney · Annet

Firebrand · St. Agnes

Plympton

Eagle · Association · Hathor · Map not to scale.

There are many beautiful unspoilt beaches on the Isles of Scilly. The white sand lapped by an azure blue sea gives the impression of being in the Caribbean. In the shallows, the sand reflects the sunlight making snorkelling or diving here a bright and enjoyable experience.

Snorkelling is a great way to explore safely the marine life found close to the shore. Without venturing out of your depth it is possible to swim over the forests of seaweed that provide shelter for fish, starfish and anemones. Bottom living fish such as sand gobies, dragonets and juvenile plaice dart across open patches of sand, while crabs scuttle between the shelter of rocks and seaweed. Shoals of sand eels and grey mullet can occasionally be seen.

In sheltered sandy bays away from the beaches, but still in less than five metres of water, there are extensive beds of eel grass. These are vibrant green and look like underwater fields of grass. Eel grass is a nationally scarce species which is more commonly found in the south west of England. The beds provide a nursery for fish and shellfish, but most importantly, eel grass is the habitat for seahorses. These have been seen in St Mary's Harbour and in Tresco Channel in the last five years.

Away from the sandy beaches the shallows are dominated by kelp forests. Kelp is a brown seaweed that can grow to a height of over two metres. As the waters around Scilly are so clear, kelp dominates rocky areas between depths of three to 22 metres. Kelp is an incredibly important part of the marine ecosystem, providing food and shelter for many species. Around the Eastern Isles, it also provides the backdrop for diving or snorkelling with seals.

All the photographs in this section have been taken in less than 12 metres of water, and the chapter begins with views from around the beaches of St Martin's.

This image to the right is typical of the shallows around St Martin's. Taken in Little Bay in two metres it shows a rocky outcrop supporting a mixed turf of red, green and brown seaweeds, with bright sandy patches behind.

The tall brown seaweed dominating the image to the left is thongweed. The tall, flattened fronds of thongweed grow out of small brown button like growths on the rocks, which look a little bit like toadstools. The fronds can grow over two metres in length.

A rock supporting red seaweeds and snakelocks anemones.

Little Bay, St Martin's

The view to the left shows a pink knobbly substance growing in the centre of the rock. This is an encrusting pink algae, which is hard and chalky and common in the shallows.

The encrusting pink algae can also grow on shells such as the one inhabited by this hermit crab.

The distinctive snakelocks anemone is common in the shallows. It has over 200 long wavy tentacles which, unusually for an anemone, cannot be fully retracted. Snakelocks anemones can be grey, brown or bright green in colour and grow up to 15cm in size. Some have bright purple tips which are a result of the presence inside the anemone of symbiotic algae. The algae are protected by the anemone, which in turn benefits from the compounds which the algae produce.

Some of the most easily recognisable crustaceans found in the shallows are hermit crabs. Hermit crabs have soft bodies and so live in discarded shells for protection. The crab is able to withdraw completely into the shell if threatened. As the crab grows it has to find bigger shells to move into. The images above show hermit crabs in a painted topshell and a flat periwinkle shell.

The photo above shows a cloak anemone, which is only ever found growing on anemone hermit crabs. The cloak anemone has very distinctive pink spots. Its white tentacles are held close to the mouth of the crab, enabling the anemone to scavenge scraps of food. The crab also benefits from the presence of the anemone. By secreting a hard residue the anemone provides an extension to the crab's shell, removing the need for it to find a larger home. The stinging tentacles of the anemone offer the hermit crab additional protection.

Other anemones that occur in the shallows include the red speckled pimplet anemone, see the two photos above. The column of this anemone is covered in rows of non sticky warts, each of which has a red dot on it. This anemone can grow up to 12cm across. It is only found in south west Britain but is commonly seen around Scilly.

The burrowing anemone is found in areas of sand and gravel and lives in a tube buried in the sediment rather than attaching itself to a hard substrate. If disturbed, the anemone will retract into its tube.

Eel grass is a nationally important species and a Biodiversity Action Plan habitat. There are many eel grass beds in the shallow areas of sheltered water around the islands. It is a flowering plant and the leaves grow up to one metre in length. The eel grass beds provide an important habitat for many species including the stalked jellyfish, above centre. This umbrella shaped creature grows up to 5cm high. Snakelocks anemones grow on the eel grass, above left, and eel grass leaves are often covered with a colonial sea squirt. The eel grass is a nursery for fish; the one seen above right is a two spotted cling fish. This photo was taken at a depth of five metres in Tean Sound, to the west of St Martin's.

The red jelly-like blobs often seen on rocks at low tide, in crevices or below overhanging areas, are beadlet anemones. As the tide rises the incoming water allows these anemones to take on their true shape. The photo left shows them in both states. Beadlet anemones are so called because there is a row of blue spots or tubercles below their ring of tentacles. These anemones are only found in very shallow water. The predominant colour is red, although they can also be green, brown or orange.

Dahlia anemones can be found in shallow areas of gravel. They are very beautiful anemones, short and squat, that can grow to a diameter of 20cm. The photo above shows the anemone retracted. In gullies, these anemones can grow in dense patches. The colours can be variable, creating the appearance of a flower bed.

Edible crabs are easily recognised by the pie crust edging to their shells and the black tipped claws on their pincers. Juvenile crabs as little as 2cm across can be found in crevices and amongst the seaweed in the shallows. In places like Tean Sound, where there is a gravel sand substrate, it is possible to see the large pits dug by the adult crabs hunting for burrowing prey. Adult edible crabs can grow up to 25cm wide.

The photo right is of a velvet swimming crab, recognisable by its red eyes and the blue lines on its legs and claws. The hind legs are flattened and covered in soft hairs. These crabs are smaller than edible crabs, growing to 7cm wide. Other crabs that can be seen in the shallows include shore crabs, broad clawed porcelain crabs and, occasionally, spiny spider crabs.

Many different types of fish can be seen in shallow water. Large adult ballan wrasse up to 60cm in length, see above left, swim amongst the seaweed close to the shore. Juvenile pollack, above right, are also a common sight. These are darker red in colour than the silvery grey adults.

Gobies are small fish that dart across shallow sandy areas. The photo bottom right is of a rock goby; these can grow up to 12cm in length. Another slightly larger fish often seen is the dragonet, see photo to the left. These fish are broader than gobies, with triangular shaped heads and colourful bodies.

Tean Sound lies to the west of St Martin's and fish such as sea scorpions can be found here, see left. These beautiful fish are generally well camouflaged. They have a large head with a long spine on the cheek and a white barbel by the mouth. They can grow up to 10cm in length. Also common among the gravel areas in Tean Sound are painted gobies, see above. This goby has dark spots along the side of its body, pale patches along its back and a row of dark marks on its dorsal fins. It is similar in size to the sea scorpion.

Little cuttle can occasionally be seen off sandy beaches; these photos were taken amongst the eel grass at the Eastern Isles. These small cuttlefish are only 2cm in length. Often it's the ink that they squirt as a decoy to predators that can be seen first before the creatures themselves.

They have an amazing ability to change the patterns on their bodies to blend in with the substrate they are swimming over. When hiding in the sand, all that can be seen of the creature is its eye.

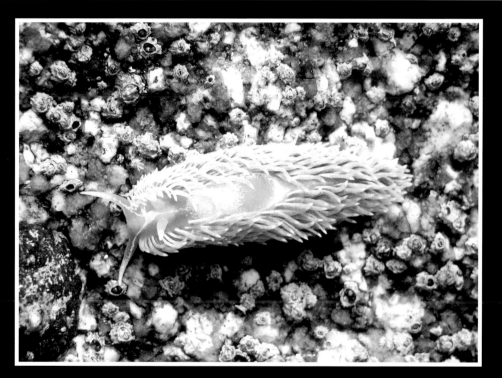

It is possible to see sea slugs in shallow waters. The sea slug shown in the photo above is *Aeolidia papillosa* and the photograph was taken in less than three metres of water. This species feeds on sea anemones.

Sea hares can also be found in the shallows. They have four tentacles on their heads and the upper pair resembles hare's ears, hence the name. They feed on seaweed and their colour depends upon the type that they eat. If threatened, sea hares will release a purple liquid as a defence mechanism. They can grow up to 20cm in length.

Kelp dominates the rocky shores from three metres down to over 20 metres. It grows prolifically in the clear waters around Scilly and individual specimens can be two metres tall. Although from above kelp forests look dull and uninteresting, they form an incredibly important habitat. All seaweeds are algae and are attached to rocks or a firm surface by a root-like structure called a holdfast.

These holdfasts become a home for anemones, sponges and sea squirts as well as providing shelter for young edible crabs, fish and squat lobsters. The Eastern Isles, where the seals live, are surrounded by kelp forests and the seals can often be seen playing and hiding in the kelp.

Although it is not possible to snorkel out to Menavaur, a rock which lies to the north of Tresco, it is a fascinating shallow area of Scilly. There is an enormous cleft running through the rock and the sheer rock faces alone make it visually impressive.

34

Due to its location, Menavaur is a surge gully and as a result of this kelp cannot grow here. Instead, the rock faces are covered with orange and white sponges and a short turf of red seaweeds which are able to withstand the surge.

Chapter 2 – Reefs

The reefs around Scilly are very different from the coral reefs found in tropical waters. There are no myriads of colourful fish or massive coral structures with turtles and sharks cruising by. The reefs are, however, as awe-inspiring, colourful and beautiful as any tropical reef.

There are many reasons why the reefs around Scilly are so spectacular. Firstly the typical typography of the islands' granite rock - sheer rock faces, enormous boulders with deep crevices - that can be seen on land continues underwater. Some walls extend for over 50 metres and are so covered in marine life that it is impossible to see the rock substrate. There are fierce tides around Scilly, with a tidal range of up to six metres. This creates very high energy sites at rock faces facing the tide. The nutrient rich water provides ideal conditions for marine life to thrive. Another big influence on the reefs is the amount of swell they receive. Lying 28 miles from the mainland, the reefs are very exposed. They are often pummelled by huge ground seas which are caused by storms coming in from the Atlantic Ocean. This affects what marine life is able to survive on the reefs. The impact of this swell is particularly noticeable on sites out to the west of the islands and at the Seven Stones which lie between Scilly and mainland Britain.

In addition, the visibility in the islands' waters is generally better than on mainland sites. Diving in visibility of up to 25 metres allows the true scale and majesty of the reefs to be appreciated.

The dominant group of animals that the reefs support are anemones. These grow prolifically in high energy areas and come in many shapes and sizes. Colours can vary from white to orange, pink, purple, yellow, green and red. Some species reproduce asexually giving rise to large patches of anemones of the same colour. This gives the reefs the appearance of flower gardens. This can be seen in the photo left, which is of Peter's Rock which lies to the east of St Martin's.

Lying between Cornwall and the Isles of Scilly, the Seven Stones is an area of exceptionally clear water and abundant marine life. The photo on the left was taken at a depth of 25 metres. Brightly coloured anemones and sponges cover most rock faces. Although more famous for it's shipwrecks, many fabulous new reefs are being discovered here.

The reefs of Scilly are probably best known for their jewel anemones. These are small squat anemones which are 2.5cm in diameter with the tentacles extended. They are found growing prolifically in areas with strong tidal flow. Jewel anemones come in many vibrant colours including pink, yellow, blue, purple and red. As they are one of the anemones that reproduce asexually, rock faces become covered with different coloured patches of the anemone.

Jewel anemones have over one hundred tentacles arranged in three concentric circles. Each tentacle has a translucent club tipped end. The anemone will feed when the tide is running and retract its tentacles during periods of slack water.

Jewel anemones can be found growing in shallow waters and down to a depth of 100 metres. They are exquisitely pretty and create spectacular underwater scenes.

Plumose anemones are often found growing profusely in areas of strong tidal flow. The colours vary, being either white, green or orangey brown. Some reefs have such an abundance of white plumose anemones covering the rocks that it looks as if it has been snowing underwater.

The photo to the far left was taken at a depth of 30 metres on Flat Ledge, a reef to the east of St Martin's. The other two photos were taken on reefs at the Western Rocks.

Plumose anemones are a tall anemone growing up to 50cm high, with a smooth column. There is a distinct collar below the crown of up to 200 tentacles. The slender tentacles give the anemone a feathery appearance. When there is no tidal flow, the anemones retract as can be seen in the photo left. These photographs were all taken on reefs off St Mary's.

The elegant anemone grows commonly on the reefs around Scilly. This anemone looks similar to a daisy and can be found in many colour forms, including all white, all pink, white and orange or variegated brown. These anemones thrive in areas of surge and the photos above were both taken on reefs at the Seven Stones.

The elegant anemone can be found in shallow waters and down to a depth of 50 metres. Each anemone has a ring of 200 tentacles and when fully extended measures 6cm across.

The photo on the far left is of a sunset cup-coral. This nationally rare species has a Biodiversity Action Plan and can be found at four locations on Scilly. It grows on vertical rock faces and is a very long lived species. The photo above left is of a scarlet and gold star-coral, another nationally scarce species that looks similar to the sunset cup-coral. These are found in shallow surge gullies and this photo was taken in the Eastern Isles. Above right, is a Devonshire cup-coral. This is a true coral similar to those that form coral reefs. However, this cup-coral grows in a solitary form. It can grow to 1.5cm in diameter and can be pink, white, green or brown.

Lobsters are easily recognisable, with a dark blue body and long red antennae, and can be found on the reefs around Scilly. They have two large differently shaped claws. One is heavier and used for crushing, the other is sharper and used for cutting. Lobsters can live up to 50 years. The one in the photo far right is an old specimen as its huge claws are well worn.

Local fisherman on Scilly have a voluntary ban on catching female lobsters that are carrying eggs, to help increase the overall lobster population. In addition, the National Lobster Hatchery in Padstow, Cornwall, has released juvenile lobsters on Scilly. The photo above middle shows the size of the juveniles when released.

58

Crawfish can be found on the deeper more exposed reefs. It is distinguishable from a lobster by its long antennae and a lack of claws. Larger specimens can be up to 50cm in length.

The creature upside down in the photo above is a spiny squat lobster. It has vivid red and blue markings on its shell and can grow to 9cm in length. It is sharing a crevice in the rock with a velvet swimming crab.

These photos were taken on reefs to the west of the islands.

Due to the big Atlantic swells experienced here, there are fewer walls of jewel anemones and more low lying colourful sponges such as the orange carrot sponge, see left.

Pink sea fans, a Biodiversity Action Plan species, can be found all around the islands. They are beautiful, delicate, slow growing gorgonian corals, which can grow up to 30cm tall. Sea fans feed by filtering suspended matter from sea water, so are only found at sites where the water movement is strong. Both the pink and white forms of the sea fan occur around Scilly.

In addition to being important in their own right, sea fans provide a habitat for two associated species. The nationally scarce sea fan nudibranch, above left, is a beautifully camouflaged sea slug closely resembling the sea fan it lives on. The sea fan anemone, above right, is classified as nationally rare. It is a small anemone, less than 10mm across.

Most sponges occur in areas that are out of the tide; the photos on this page were all taken below 20 metres. The photo left is of a large yellow branching sponge. The volcano sponge, above, is more typical of an exposed ocean reef. The photo top right shows a yellow hedgehog sponge and a chimney sponge with a bloody henry starfish. The giant boring sponge, bottom right, is bright yellow and can grow up to a metre in size.

66

Red fingers are a colonial soft coral found in less tidal areas of reefs. The slender red fleshy lobes of the body can grow up to 30cm in length. The white polyps emerge to filter food from the surrounding water. When retracted, the red fingers have a knobbly appearance, as can be seen in the photo above. This species is only found on the south and west coastlines of Britain.

The yellow cluster anemone is a nationally scarce colonial anemone. Each polyp, which is 1-2cm tall, has two circles of 26-34 yellow tentacles. This species can be found at 13 sites on Scilly.

The white cluster anemone is very similar to the yellow cluster anemone. It is nationally scarce and can be found at six locations on Scilly. It is a larger anemone and the polyps have 34-44 tentacles.

Sea slugs are molluscs, similar to the slugs found on land but much more beautiful. Sea slugs eat sponges and hydroids and are found on most reefs. They tend to be more common in May, when they can be seen laying their eggs which resemble coiled white ribbons, see photo above left. The crystal sea slug, top right, can grow to 70mm in length. The photo left is of a yellow edged polycera sea slug.

The photo above is of a sponge sea slug. This resembles a sponge, is 45mm in size and is classified as nationally scarce. It has been seen on nine reefs on Scilly.

The photo right was taken in September 2008. It is of the sea slug *Discodoris rosi*. This was the first recording ever of this sea slug in UK waters. It is a species that is found in waters off Portugal and Spain; the furthest north it had been recorded was Brittany. It was seen on three sites around the islands and this photo was taken on a reef to the west of St Mary's.

Fish do occur on the reefs around Scilly, but never in the dense numbers that are seen on coral reefs. The most spectacular fish is the cuckoo wrasse, which can be found at depth of 20-80 metres. The male can grow to 35cm in length and is beautifully marked with bright orange and turquoise blue. The females, see photo above right, are less colourful. Male cuckoo wrasse are an inquisitive, territorial fish that will come close to divers, sometimes close enough to nibble fingers.

The fish, above and left, is a red blenny. This fish is normally found off the coasts of western Ireland and Scotland. It is similar to the tompot blenny, see far right, but is redder in colour. The red blenny can be found in crevices on reefs and grows up to 12cm in length. Both species have characteristic thick lips and feathery tentacles around the nostrils and between the eyes. They are highly photogenic.

The leopard spotted goby, see left, is a distinctive fish, covered in large dark spots. They can often be seen darting into crevices on reefs, as they are fairly shy.

Other fish often found on reefs include the small spotted catshark, commonly known as dogfish, see top right. This small shark can grow up to a metre in length.

The photo bottom right is of a lemon sole. This bottom-dwelling fish can found on stony seabeds from depths of 20 to 200 metres.

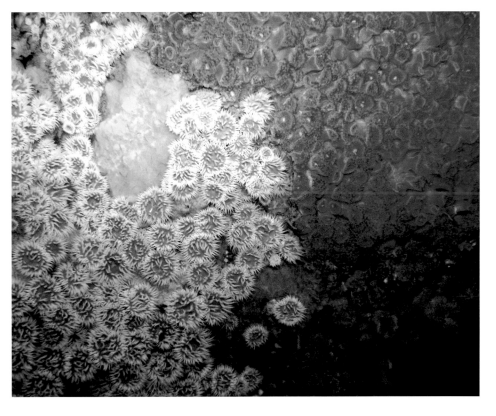

The reefs around Scilly can rival any tropical reef for colour, beauty and variety of marine life. By carrying out exploratory diving, the authors are always finding new and exciting dive sites. All these photos were taken on recently discovered reefs.

Chapter 3 – Wrecks

The Isles of Scilly are renowned for shipwrecks. The treacherous island waters have become the final resting place for many hundreds of ships. The most famous of which are, probably, the wrecks of the Association fleet off the Western Rocks. Four ships, the Association, the Romney, the Eagle and the Firebrand, were all lost on October 22nd 1707 with the loss of 1,673 lives. This still remains Britain's worst naval peacetime disaster. A prize was put up by the government of the day to discover an accurate means of measuring longitude as a result of this terrible tragedy. Another famous wreck is the Hollandia, a Dutch East Indiaman which sank in 1743 with a cargo of silver coins. There is very little left now of the structure of these old wooden ships, but what does remain are artefacts such as cannons, cannon balls and anchors.

The islands' waters are very exposed and the power of the sea in a big Atlantic storm is incredible. As a result, the wrecks around Scilly are generally no longer boat shaped or like a cartoon image of a shipwreck. For many, the decks have collapsed and it's the large structures such as steering quadrants, engines and boilers that dominate the wreckage. Wrecks themselves are not permanent features and continually suffer from erosion and decay. In 2004, during a big south easterly gale, the waters off St Agnes above the wreck of the Hathor boiled with rusty water. After being underwater for 84 years, the housing surrounding the propeller shaft succumbed to the power of the sea and collapsed.

Some ships have sunk in areas where there are strong tidal currents. These have effectively become artificial reefs. Wrecks like the King Cadwallon, to the east of St Martin's, and the Cita which was wrecked on Newfoundland Point in 1997, are now a mass of marine life. For divers, this adds to the enjoyment of diving on a wreck.

The King Cadwallon sank on 22nd July 1906 on the Hard Lewis Rocks which lie to the east of St Martin's. She was carrying a cargo of coal and was bound for Naples. The rocks of the Hard Lewis rise steeply from deep water. It was a foggy day and despite taking regular depth soundings the King Cadwallon foundered on the rocks. The photo far left shows the steering quadrant, which is part of the stern of the ship and lies in 42 metres. The quadrant is over four metres high and is covered in plumose anemones.

The photo to the left is a view of the stern of the wreck. This part of the wreck lies in an area of strong tides and it is impossible to find an inch of it that is not smothered in marine life.

87

The engine of the King Cadwallon lies in 25 metres of water. The photo on the far left is of a large open lattice-type structure which is attached to the engine. It is big enough for divers to be able to swim through it. This section of the wreck is covered in plumose anemones.

The photo on the left is of the conrods from the engine. Above, is a view taken from the bow of the ship. This wreckage lies in 14 metres of water and the photo shows the bulkheads of the hull. There is less tide in this area so there is less life on this section of the wreck. The white soft corals seen in the photo are dead men's fingers.

The Seven Stones reef lies between Cornwall and the Isles of Scilly. It is a notoriously dangerous area for shipping and is where the Torrey Canyon was wrecked in March 1967.

The wreck of the Barreman lies to the north of the reef. She was lost with all hands on 9th July 1887 whilst en route from South Shields to San Francisco. Her cargo included bricks, above right, and cement. The photo to the far left was taken at 30 metres. It shows wreckage including a winch, scattered bricks and barrel shaped objects. The cargo of cement was carried in barrels and over time these have been eaten away, leaving the cement set in the shape of barrels.

There is little life on this wreck as it does not lie in an area of strong tides. Species such as dead men's fingers can be seen growing on the bollards. The water around the Seven Stones is very clear, allowing kelp to grow at a depth of 30 metres.

Wrecks provide an excellent habitat for marine life. Conger eels can often be found hiding within them. These photos were taken on the wreck of the Empire. She was a steamer that sank in Broad Sound on 26th November 1860. Little remains of the wreck now except the engine, part of which has become the home to a conger eel.

In the photos above it can be seen that there are several prawns close to the entrance of the conger's home. These prawns are waiting for scraps of food from the conger's prey.

The Cita was wrecked on Newfoundland Point, St Mary's, in the early hours of 26th March 1997. She was a container ship on her way to Ireland. The crew had set a course and then fallen asleep. The containers that were washed ashore held a wide range of products, including computer mice, trainers, tobacco, plastic bags, golf bags and wooden flooring. Before she could be salvaged the Cita broke in two and sank.

The photo left was taken of the bow section of the Cita in the year that she sank and her name is clearly visible. The photo right shows the bow ten years later, now covered in marine life.

The stern section of the Cita, which includes the accommodation block, now lies in 35 metres of water. This is in an area of strong tides, so all the surfaces, railings and cables are now smothered in anemones and sponges.

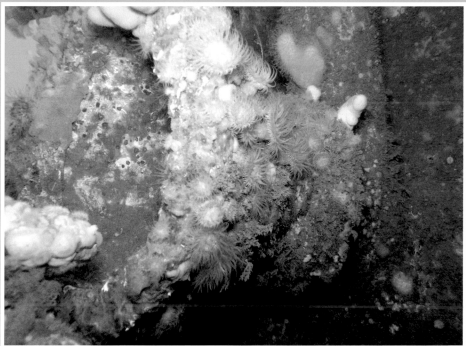

The Lethagus Rocks to the south west of St Agnes have claimed two ships, the Hathor and the Plympton, whose wrecks now lie across each other. The Hathor was a German steamer which sank on 2nd December 1920. The photo far left is of the hull of the Hathor close to the bow at 38 metres. This section of the wreck is smothered in plumose anemones.

The photo above left is part of the engine. Above right, shows what will happen to a toilet after nearly 100 years underwater. As often happens with wrecks, it is now lying at an unusual angle.

The Plympton sank on 14th August 1909. She lies upside down on the seabed. The photo to the left is of the railings taken in 35 metres of water. The photos below are of the Plympton's upturned hull. This is one of the best locations on Scilly for potato crisp bryozoans and pink sea fans. Both species are very delicate and slow growing, which makes them particularly vulnerable to any forms of disturbance. Pink sea fans can grow in a white form and both colours can be seen on the Plympton.

The Hollandia was lost off St Agnes on her maiden voyage on 13th July 1743. She was carrying a cargo of silver coins. All that remains of the wreck, which lies in 30 metres of water, are the cannons and anchors. The photo below shows an edible crab which has set up home in the mouth of one of the cannons from the wreck.

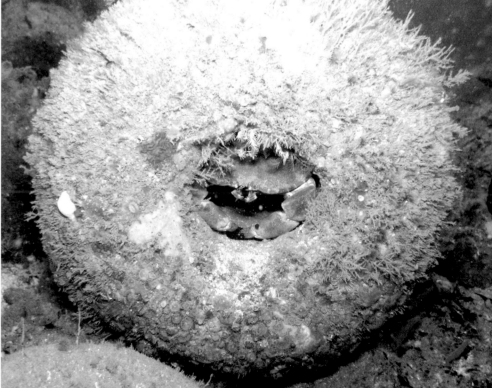

Chapter 4 – Seals

There is a large colony of grey seals on Scilly. They can always be found around the Eastern Isles and at the Western Rocks during the summer months. The grey seal is a protected animal and is listed in the EC Habitats Directive. The UK's grey seals represent 38% of the world's population of this species. The majority of these are found in Scotland, which increases the importance of the seal colony on Scilly.

Seals will haul themselves out of the sea and onto rocks as the tide drops. They then spend the low water basking until the incoming tide covers the rocks and washes them back into the water. On land, seals look quite ungainly, like large lumps of blubber. However, when underwater, seals are both incredibly graceful and agile.

The Cornwall Seal Group has been carrying out a photo identification project with the seals around Scilly and Cornwall. One seal has been photographed off the Eastern Isles and three days later identified over forty miles away off Godrevy on the north coast of Cornwall. The information collected by the Cornwall Seal Group helps in mapping populations and in understanding more about the behaviour of seals.

It is possible to go diving and snorkelling with the seals. They are very inquisitive animals and will often come close to those in the water. It is an amazing experience to be with them in their natural environment. The seals are always in charge of the encounters and being so nimble in the water, it would be impossible for a human to get close to a seal that didn't want to be approached. If in the mood to play, the seals will generally approach from behind and sometimes will nibble the fins of divers and snorkellers. When seals interact with humans it can be hard sometimes to say who is entertaining whom.

This short final chapter is a shameless indulgence of photos of these charming and endearing creatures.

Seals are incredibly agile underwater. Often, with a quick movement of a flipper, they are able to speed through the water or change direction with extraordinary ease. They can change their body shape and become streamlined if speed is required. Seals can just as easily hang motionless in the water.

Seals are often quite curious about underwater cameras. Both these images were taken just before the seals got close enough to explore the camera with their mouths.

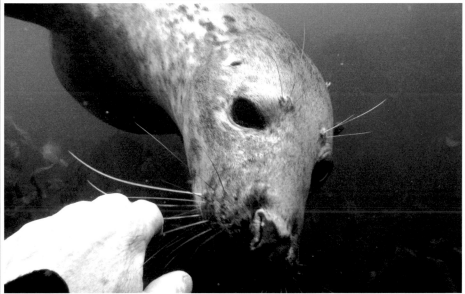

Seals will happily interact with divers and snorkellers. Despite humans being in their environment, the seals never show aggression. They seem to be fascinated by fins and will spend a lot of time investigating and nibbling at them. Sometimes, the seals will come extremely close to divers and appear to enjoy being stroked.

Often the best time to snorkel with seals is on an ebbing tide. The seals will swim around in the shallows waiting for the rocks to uncover. Whilst waiting for this to happen, the seals will happily interact with snorkellers. Once hauled out of the water, seals become quite territorial about their rocks. They can often be heard calling to each other, letting other seals know just who's in charge of the rock.

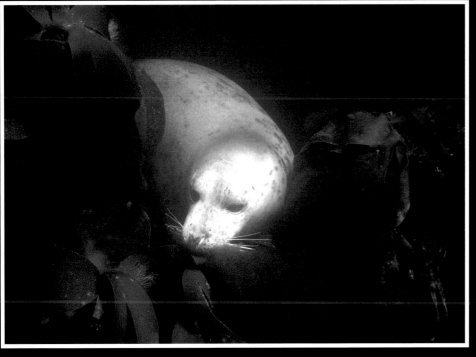 

Kelp dominates the underwater areas where the seals live. They will often lie up
in favourite crevices and gullies under the kelp. They can spend up to 20 minutes

Seals are beautiful, graceful creatures. Their large puppy dog eyes and willingness to interact with humans underwater make them the highlight of many a divers' visit to the islands.